Ages **6–7**

Schofield&Sims

Rapid Reasoning Tests

Non-verbal Reasoning 1

11+

Name

Welcome to this book

This book gives you practice in answering non-verbal reasoning questions. The questions are like the questions in the 11+ and other school tests. You must find the correct answers.

School tests like these are often timed. So you must work quickly. An adult will time you.

All the questions in this book are multiple choice. You read the question. Then you are given some possible answers. Only one of the answers is correct. Each answer has a letter under it. You choose the answer you think is correct. Then you draw a circle round the letter under it.

What you need

- A pencil
- An eraser
- A clock, watch or stopwatch
- An adult to time how long you take and to mark the test

What to do

- Turn to **Section 1 Test 1** on page 4.
- Look at the blue box. It is near the top of the first page. It says **Target time**. This tells you how long the test should take.
- The adult who is helping you will tell you when to start the test.
- Find this blue arrow ⬇. It is near the top of the first page. Start each test here.
- Find this square ■. The words beside it tell you what to do for this sort of question. They give you instructions. Read them carefully.
- Look below the instructions. Read the **Example**. Look at the letters below the possible answers. Find the letter with the circle round it. This answer is correct. Work out why it is correct.
- Use a similar method to answer question 1. Do your best. Work quickly.
- Try to answer every question. But if you do get stuck on a question, leave it. Go on to the next one.
- Finish the first page. Then go on to the second page. The question type may change.
- When you reach the words **End of test**, stop. Tell the adult that you have finished.
- The adult will mark your test. Then the adult will fill in the boxes at the end of the test.
- Did you get some questions wrong? Do not look at the correct answers. Just try these questions again. Then ask the adult to check.
- Later you will do more tests. You will soon find the correct answers more quickly. The adult will tell you what to do next.

Published by Schofield & Sims Ltd,
Dogley Mill, Fenay Bridge, Huddersfield HD8 0NQ, UK
Telephone 01484 607080
www.schofieldandsims.co.uk
Second impression 2014
Copyright © Schofield & Sims Ltd, 2014

Author: Rebecca Brant. Rebecca Brant has asserted her moral right under the Copyright, Designs and Patents Act, 1988, to be identified as the author of this work.

British Library Cataloguing in Publication Data. A catalogue record for this book is available from the British Library.

Commissioned by **Carolyn Richardson Publishing Services** (www.publiserve.co.uk)
Design by **Oxford Designers & Illustrators**
Front cover design by **Ledgard Jepson Ltd**
Printed in the UK by **The Lavenham Press Ltd**, Suffolk
ISBN 978 07217 1226 0

Contents

A **pull-out answers section** (pages A1 to A8) appears in the centre of this book, between pages 20 and 21. It also gives simple guidance on how best to use this book. Remove this section before you begin working through the tests.

■ Which picture on the right belongs to the group on the left? Circle the letter.

Example

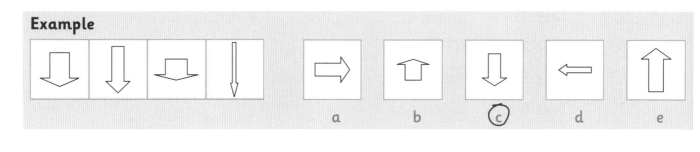

1.

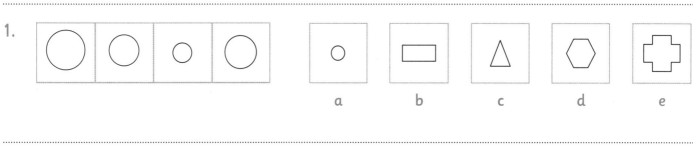

2.

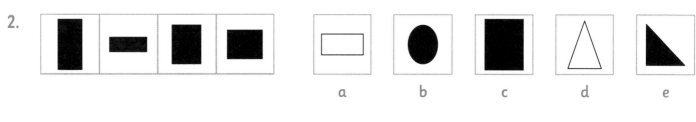

3.

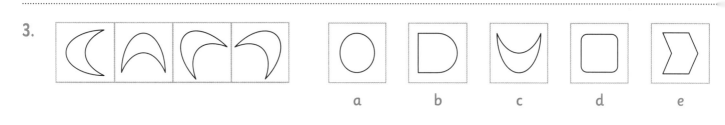

4.

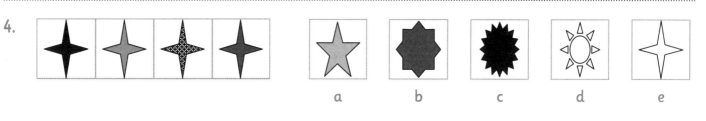

5.

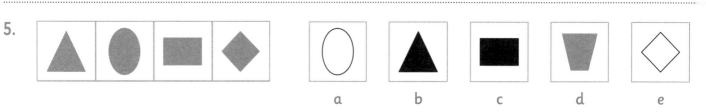

Now go on to the next page. ➡

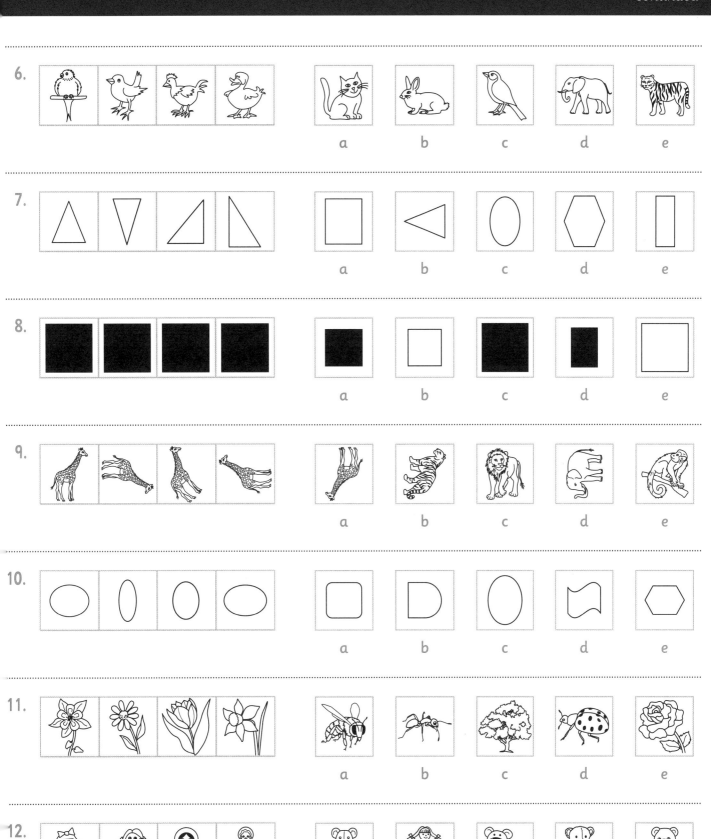

6.

7.

8.

9.

10.

11.

12.

End of test.

| Score: | Time taken: | Target met? |

Rapid Reasoning Tests | Schofield & Sims

Non-verbal Reasoning 1   5

Target time: **5 minutes**

■ Which picture is the odd one out? Circle the letter.

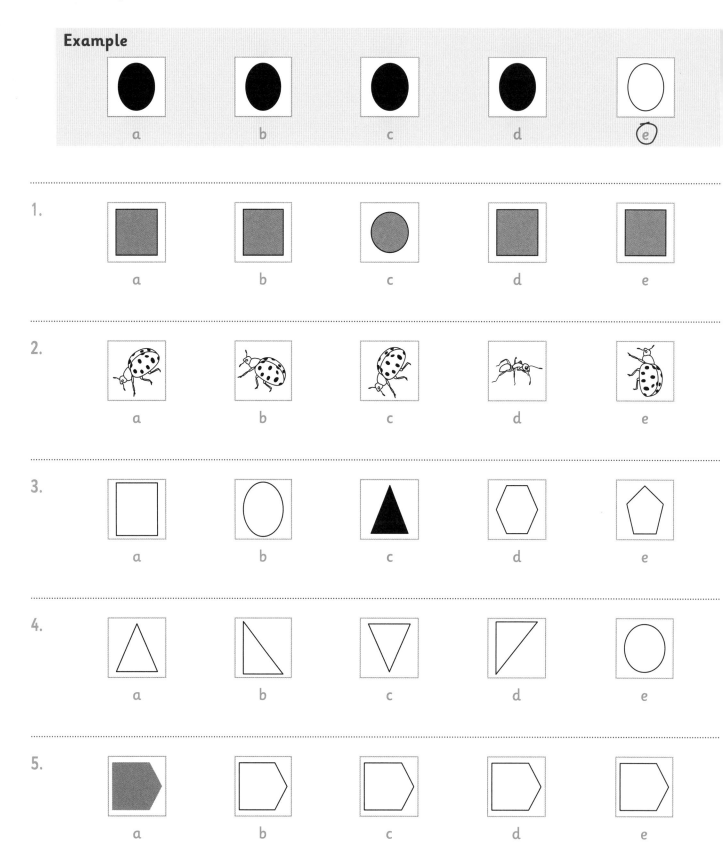

Example

a   b   c   d   e

1.

a   b   c   d   e

2.

a   b   c   d   e

3.

a   b   c   d   e

4.

a   b   c   d   e

5.

a   b   c   d   e

Now go on to the next page. ➡

6.

    a   b   c   d   e

7.

    a   b   c   d   e

8.

    a   b   c   d   e

9.

    a   b   c   d   e

10.

    a   b   c   d   e

11.

    a   b   c   d   e

12.

    a   b   c   d   e

End of test.

Score:		Time taken:		Target met?	

Target time: **5 minutes**

The first two pictures go together. Which of the five pictures on the right goes with the third picture in the same way? Circle the letter.

Example

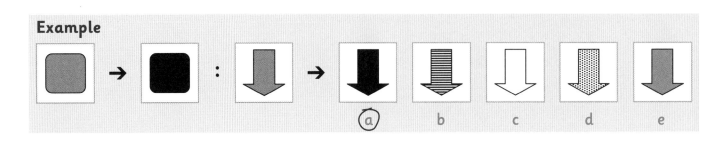

1.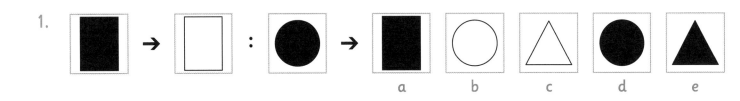

2.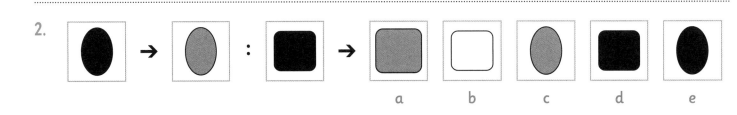

3.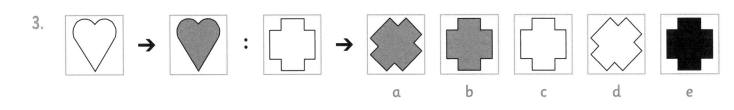

4.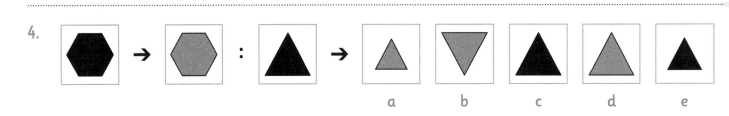

5.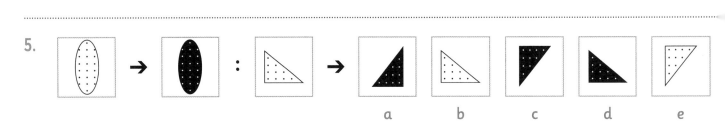

Now go on to the next page.

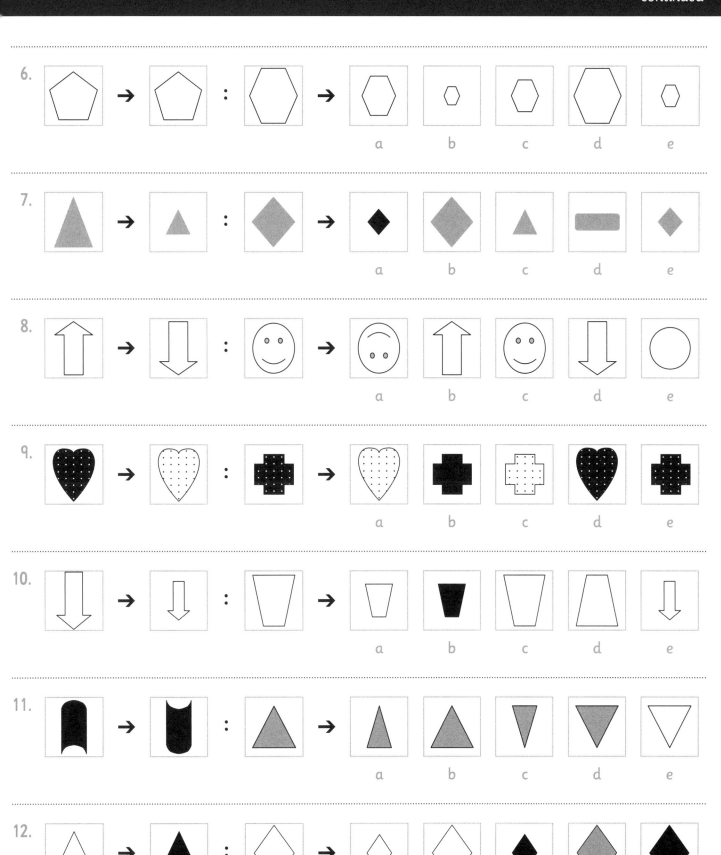

6.
a   b   c   d   e

7.
a   b   c   d   e

8.
a   b   c   d   e

9.
a   b   c   d   e

10.
a   b   c   d   e

11.
a   b   c   d   e

12.
a   b   c   d   e

End of test.

Score:		Time taken:		Target met?	

Target time: **5 minutes**

 Which of the pictures on the right goes in the empty space? Circle the letter.

Example

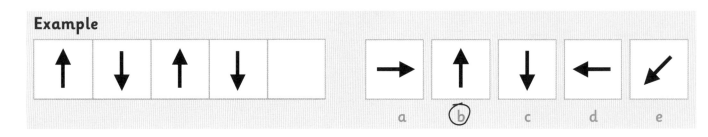

1.

a   b   c   d   e

2.

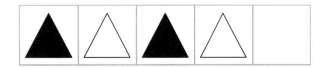

a   b   c   d   e

3.

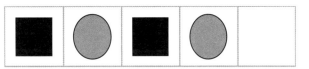

a   b   c   d   e

4.

a   b   c   d   e

5.

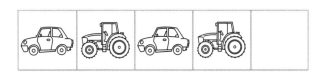

a   b   c   d   e

Now go on to the next page. ➡

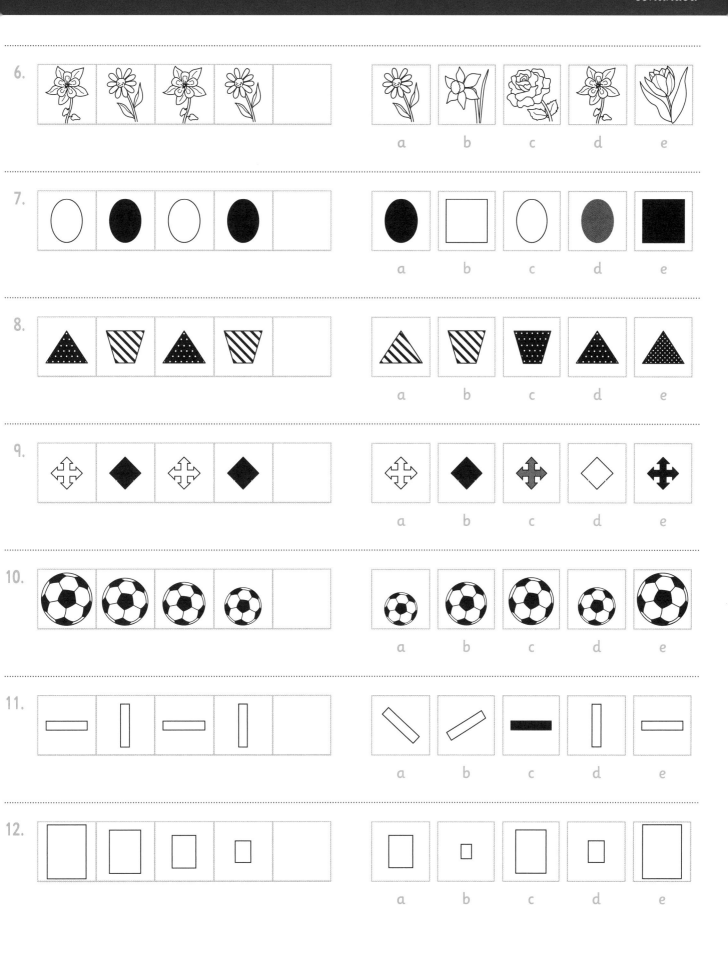

6.

7.

8.

9.

10.

11.

12.

End of test.

| Score: | | Time taken: | | Target met? | |

Rapid Reasoning Tests | Schofield & Sims

Section 1 Test 5

Target time: **5 minutes**

In which picture on the right is the picture on the left hidden? Circle the letter.

Example

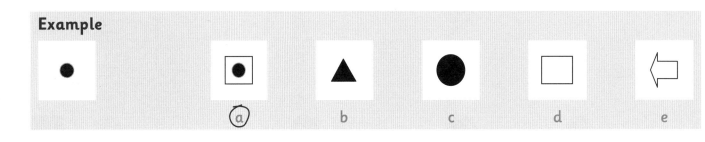

1.

                 a   b   c   d   e

2.

                 a   b   c   d   e

3.

                 a   b   c   d   e

4.

                 a   b   c   d   e

5.

                 a   b   c   d   e

Now go on to the next page. ➡

12 Non-verbal Reasoning 1   **Schofield & Sims | Rapid Reasoning Tests**

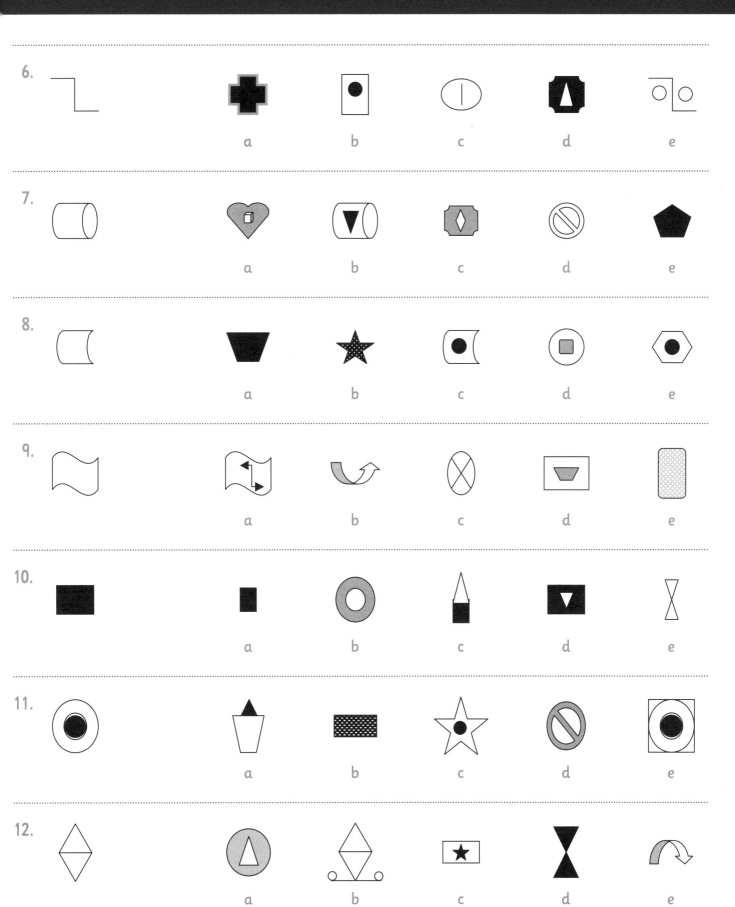

6.

    a   b   c   d   e

7.

    a   b   c   d   e

8.

    a   b   c   d   e

9.

    a   b   c   d   e

10.

    a   b   c   d   e

11.

    a   b   c   d   e

12.

    a   b   c   d   e

End of test.

Score:		Time taken:		Target met?	

Target time: **5 minutes**

Pretend the dotted line is a mirror. Which picture on the right is a reflection of the picture on the left? Circle the letter.

Example

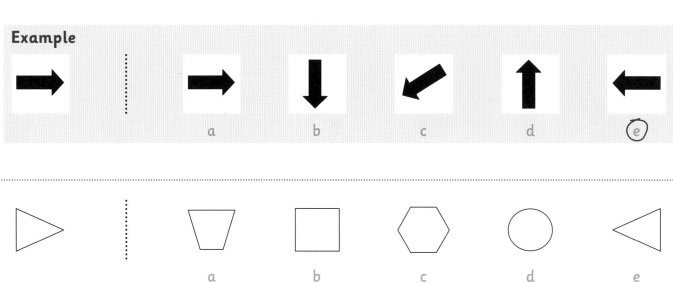

1.

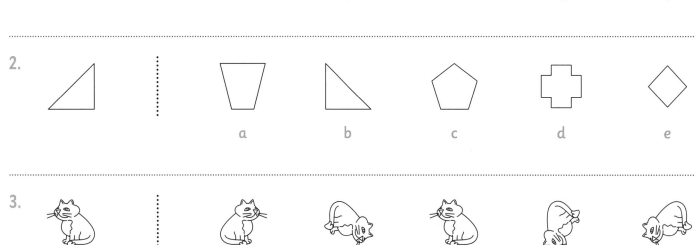

2.

3.

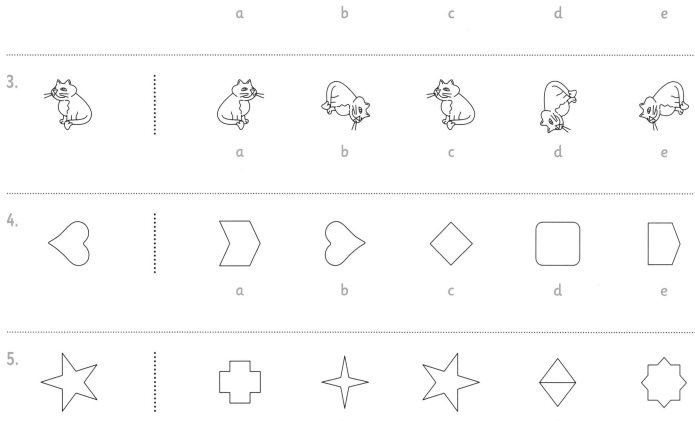

4.

5.

Now go on to the next page. ➡

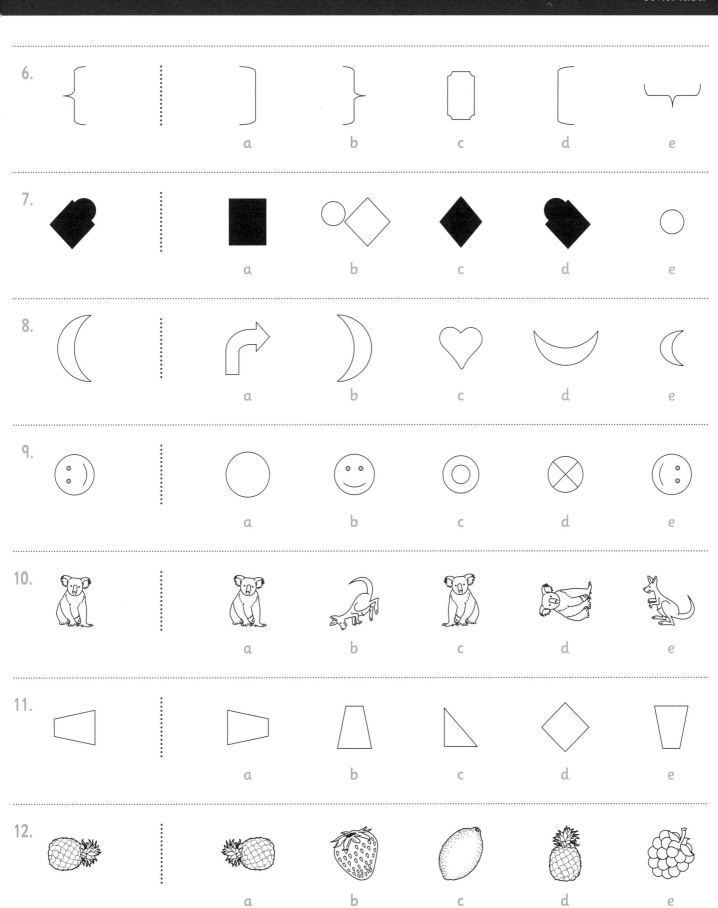

6.

a   b   c   d   e

7.

a   b   c   d   e

8.

a   b   c   d   e

9.

a   b   c   d   e

10.

a   b   c   d   e

11.

a   b   c   d   e

12.

a   b   c   d   e

End of test.

Score:		Time taken:		Target met?	

Target time: **5 minutes**

Which picture on the right belongs to the group on the left? Circle the letter.

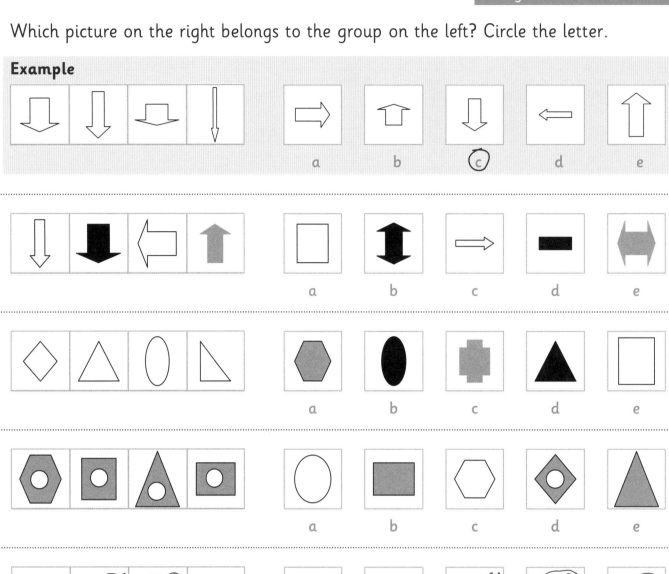

Example

a   b   c   d   e

1.

   a   b   c   d   e

2.

   a   b   c   d   e

3.

   a   b   c   d   e

4.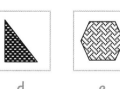

   a   b   c   d   e

5.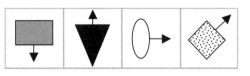

   a   b   c   d   e

6.

   a   b   c   d   e

Now go on to the next page. ➡

■ Which picture is the odd one out? Circle the letter.

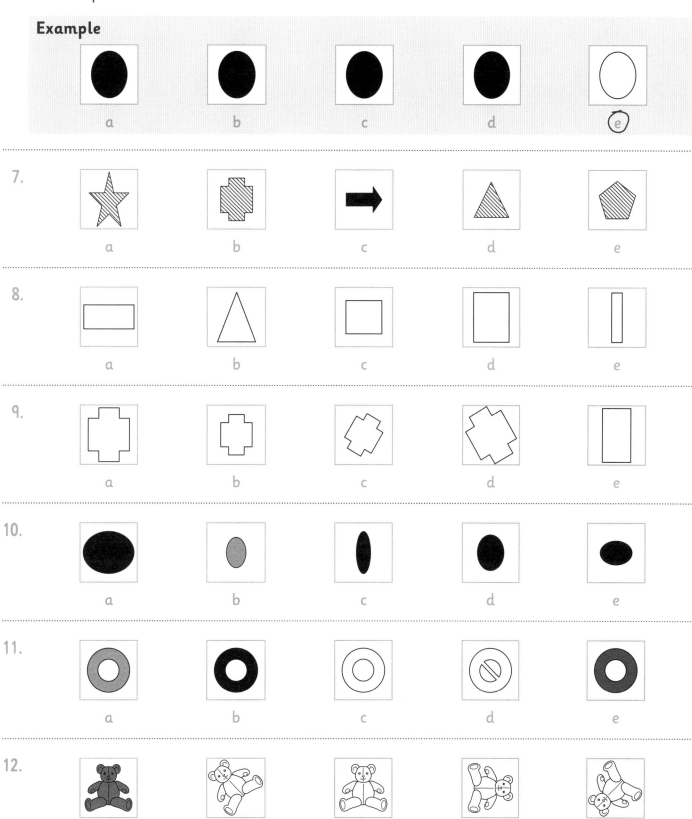

Example

| a | b | c | d | e |

7.

| a | b | c | d | e |

8.

| a | b | c | d | e |

9.

| a | b | c | d | e |

10.

| a | b | c | d | e |

11.

| a | b | c | d | e |

12.

| a | b | c | d | e |

End of test.

| Score: | Time taken: | Target met? |

Which picture is the odd one out? Circle the letter.

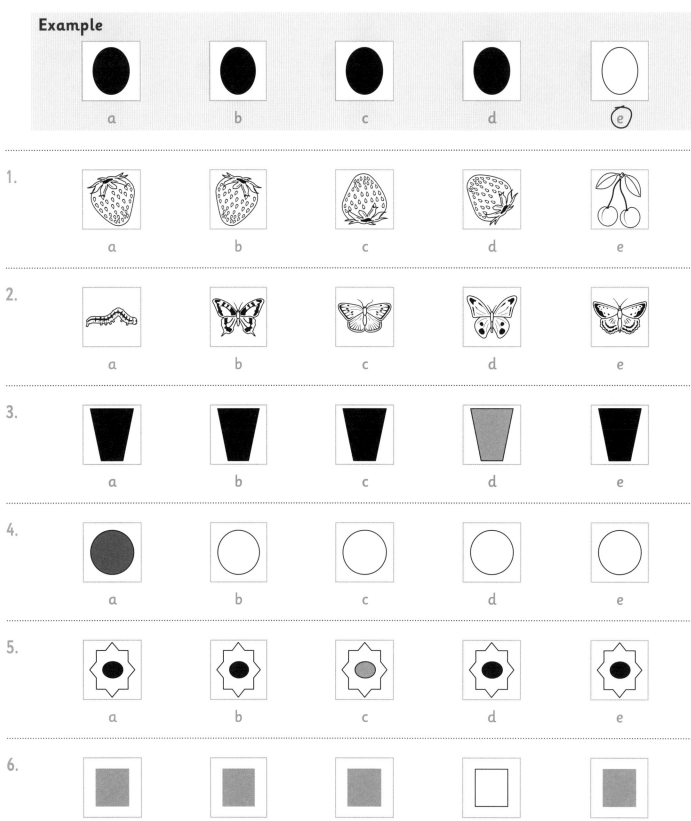

Now go on to the next page. ➡

The first two pictures go together. Which of the five pictures on the right goes with the third picture in the same way? Circle the letter.

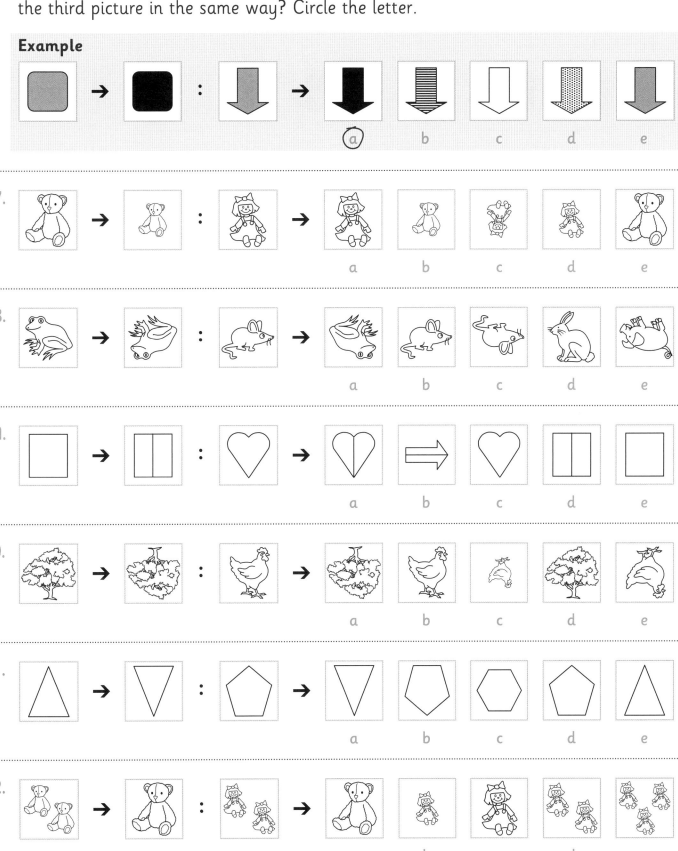

Example

7.

8.

9.

10.

11.

12.

End of test.

Score:	Time taken:	Target met?

The first two pictures go together. Which of the five pictures on the right goes with the third picture in the same way? Circle the letter.

Example

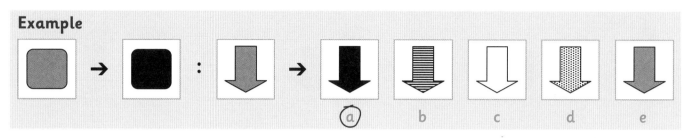

1.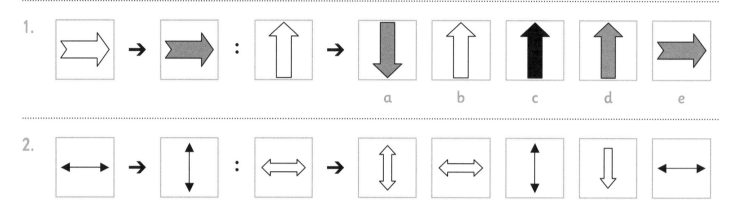

2.

3.

4.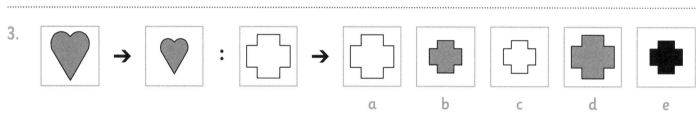

5.

6.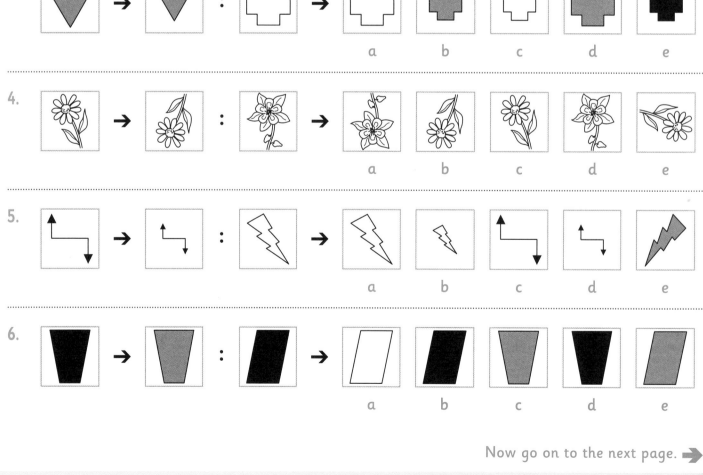

Now go on to the next page. ➡

Notes for parents, tutors, teachers and other adult helpers

- **Non-verbal Reasoning 1** is designed for six- and seven-year-olds, but may also be suitable for some older children.

- Remove this pull-out section before giving the book to the child.

- Before the child begins work on the first test, together read the instructions headed **What to do** on page 2. As you do so, point out to the child the different elements in **Section 1 Test 1**.

- Make sure that the child understands how to answer multiple choice questions and has a pencil and eraser. Also ensure that the child is able to see a clock or a watch.

- **Sections 2 and 3**: Please note that, from page 16 onwards, there are **two** types of question in each test, rather than just one as in Section 1. The question type appearing on the right-hand page of each test is different from that appearing on the left-hand page. Make sure that the child is aware of this and that he or she continues with the second page of questions as previously, without waiting.

- Be sure that the child knows to tell you clearly when he or she has finished the test.

- When the child is ready, say 'Start the test now' and make a note of the start time.

- When the child has finished, make a note of the end time and then work out how long he or she took to complete the test. Then fill in the **Time taken** box, which appears at the end of the test.

- Mark the child's work using this pull-out section, giving one mark for each correct answer. Then complete the **Score** box at the end of the test.

- This table shows you how to mark the **Target met?** box and the **Action** notes help you to plan the next step. However, these are suggestions only. Please use your own judgement as you decide how best to proceed.

Score	Time taken	Target met?	Action
1–6	Any	Not yet	Provide help and support as needed.
7–9	Any	Not yet	Encourage the child to keep practising using the tests in this book. The child may need to repeat some tests. If so, wait a few weeks or the child may simply remember the correct answers. Provide help and support as needed.
10–12	Over target – child took too long	Not yet	
10–12	On target – child took suggested time or less	Yes	Encourage the child to keep practising using further tests in this book, and to move on to the next book when you think this is appropriate.

- Whatever the test score, always encourage the child to have another go at the questions that he or she got wrong – without looking at the solutions. If the child's answers are still incorrect, work through these questions together. Demonstrate the correct method if necessary.

- If the child struggles with particular question types, help him or her to develop the strategies needed.

The **Understanding Reasoning** series, also available from Schofield & Sims, provides clear explanations on how to answer reasoning questions. It also provides 'Tips for tests' and 'Tips for revision'. For further details on this and other series that help children and young people to prepare for school selection tests, and for free downloads relating to the **Rapid Reasoning Tests**, visit www.schofieldandsims.co.uk

Answers

Section 1 Test 1 (pages 4–5)

1. a Each picture contains a circle.
2. c Each picture contains a black four-sided shape.
3. c Each picture contains a crescent moon shape.
4. e Each picture contains a four-point star.
5. d Each picture contains a grey shape.
6. c Each picture contains a bird.
7. b Each picture contains a triangle.
8. c Each picture contains a square of exactly the same size and colour.
9. a Each picture contains a giraffe.
10. c Each picture contains an oval.
11. e Each picture contains a flower.
12. b Each picture contains a doll.

Section 1 Test 2 (pages 6–7)

1. c The others are all squares.
2. d The others are all ladybirds.
3. c The others are all white.
4. e The others are all triangles.
5. a The others are all white.
6. a The others are all black.
7. b The others are all made from a broken line.
8. b The others are all upright crosses.
9. a The others are all cars.
10. d The others are all teddy bears.
11. e The others are all hearts.
12. b The others are all cats.

Section 1 Test 3 (pages 8–9)

1. b The shape stays the same but changes from black to white.
2. a The shape stays the same but changes from black to grey.
3. b The shape stays the same but changes from white to grey.
4. d The shape stays the same but changes from black to grey.
5. d The shape stays the same but changes from white with black spots to black with white spots.
6. d It is exactly the same shape and size.

7. e The shape gets smaller but stays the same colour.
8. a The same shape is shown upside down.
9. c The shape stays the same but changes from black with white spots to white with black spots.
10. a The shape gets smaller but stays the same colour.
11. d The same shape is shown upside down but stays the same colour.
12. e The shape and size stay the same but changes from white to black.

Section 1 Test 4 (pages 10–11)

1. b dog, cat, dog, cat, **dog**
2. a black triangle, white triangle, black triangle, white triangle, **black triangle**
3. b black square, grey circle, black square, grey circle, **black square**
4. d white sun, lightning bolt, white sun, lightning bolt, **white sun**
5. a car, tractor, car, tractor, **car**
6. d pointed flower, daisy flower, pointed flower, daisy flower, **pointed flower**
7. c white oval, black oval, white oval, black oval, **white oval**
8. d black triangle with white spots, striped trapezium, black triangle with same white spots, striped trapezium, **black triangle with same white spots**
9. a white arrow cross, black rhombus, white arrow cross, black rhombus, **white arrow cross**
10. a The footballs get **smaller**.
11. e white horizontal rectangle, white vertical rectangle, white horizontal rectangle, white vertical rectangle, **white horizontal rectangle**
12. b The rectangles get **smaller**.

Answers

■ Section 1 Test 5 (pages 12–13)

1. d

2. b

3. c

4. b

5. a

6. e

7. b

8. c

9. a

10. d

11. e

12. b

■ Section 1 Test 6 (pages 14–15)

1. e

2. b

3. a

4. b

5. c

6. b

7. d

8. b

9. e

10. c

11. a

12. a

Answers

Section 2 Test 1 (pages 16–17)

1. c Each picture contains a single-headed arrow.
2. e Each picture contains a white shape.
3. d Each picture contains a grey shape with a white circle inside.
4. a Each picture contains a reptile.
5. e Each picture contains the same pattern.
6. d Each picture contains a shape with an arrow joined to it.
7. c The others are all striped.
8. b The others are all rectangles.
9. e The others are all crosses.
10. b The others are all black.
11. d The others do not have a split circle.
12. a The others are all white teddy bears.

Section 2 Test 2 (pages 18–19)

1. e The others are all strawberries.
2. a The others are all butterflies.
3. d The others are all black.
4. a The others are all white.
5. c The others all contain black ovals.
6. d The others are all grey.
7. d The doll gets smaller and stays sitting up.
8. c The same picture is shown upside down (reflected).
9. a The shape stays the same but has a line down the middle.
10. e The same picture is shown upside down (reflected).
11. b The same shape is shown upside down.
12. c Two small pictures become one big one.

Section 2 Test 3 (pages 20–21)

1. d The shape stays the same but changes from white to grey.
2. a The same double-headed arrow changes from horizontal to vertical.
3. c The shape stays the same colour but gets smaller.
4. a The same flower is shown upside down (reflected).
5. b The picture stays the same but gets smaller.

6. e The shape stays the same but changes from black to grey.
7. d Each picture contains a curved arrow.
8. b Each picture contains an arrow.
9. c Each picture contains a striped shape.
10. c Each picture contains a cross.
11. c Each picture contains a pentagon.
12. e Each picture contains a rectangle.

Section 2 Test 4 (pages 22–23)

1. d big sheep facing left, two small sheep, big sheep facing left, two small sheep, **big sheep facing left**
2. e upright boy, upright girl, upright boy, upright girl, **upright boy**
3. a left-facing white arrow, right-facing black arrow, left-facing white arrow, right-facing black arrow, **left-facing white arrow**
4. c strawberry, apple, strawberry, apple, **strawberry**
5. e The crosses get **smaller**.
6. c white four-point star, grey five-point star, white four-point star, grey five-point star, **white four-point star**

7. b

8. e

9. b

10. d

11. d

12. b

Section 2 Test 5 (pages 24–25)

1. d

2. a

3. a

4. c

5. e

6. e

7. c

8. d

9. e

10. e

11. b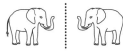

12. b

Section 2 Test 6 (pages 26–27)

1. a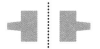

2. d

3. b

4. c

5. e

6. b

7. e right way up, upside down, right way up, upside down, **right way up**

8. b A **rectangle is added** each time.

9. c trainer, boot, trainer, boot, **trainer**

10. a The squares get **lighter**.

11. d white arrow pointing up, white arrow pointing down, white arrow pointing up, white arrow pointing down, **white arrow pointing up**

12. a smiley face, upside down smiley face, smiley face, upside down smiley face, **smiley face**

Answers

- ## Section 3 Test 1 (pages 28–29)

1. **d** Each picture contains a tree.
2. **b** Each picture contains the same shape.
3. **a** Each picture contains a smiley face.
4. **d** Each picture contains a black shape.
5. **e** Each picture contains a spotted arrow.
6. **b** Each picture contains a flying insect with wings.
7. **c** The others all have two arrows.
8. **b** The others all have the same pattern.
9. **c** The others are all single-headed arrows.
10. **b** The others all have two sweets.
11. **d** The others are all stars.
12. **d** The others all have three stars.

- ## Section 3 Test 2 (pages 30–31)

1. **d** The others all have one piece of fruit.
2. **a** The others all have five suns.
3. **d** The others all have stripes.
4. **e** The others all have handles/are made of china.
5. **b** The others all have stripes running from top left to bottom right.
6. **d** The others all have four sides.
7. **b** The shape has been cut in half vertically.
8. **e** The black shape becomes white and the white circle becomes black.
9. **c** The shape becomes smaller and black.
10. **c** The outer shape becomes black and the inner shape becomes white.
11. **b** The top half of the shape becomes black.
12. **a** The picture is a reflection.

- ## Section 3 Test 3 (pages 32–33)

1. **c** The outer shape becomes black and the inner shape becomes white.
2. **b** The picture is a reflection.
3. **e** The shape has turned upside down and become grey.
4. **a** The stripes run in the opposite direction.
5. **a** The two shapes fit together to make a new shape.
6. **b** The picture turns 90° clockwise.
7. **c** Each picture contains the same two shapes in different sizes.

8. **d** Each picture contains two cherries and one leaf of the same size.
9. **a** Each picture contains a single-headed zig-zag arrow.
10. **d** Each picture contains a square with a grey shape inside.
11. **b** Each picture contains a diamond-shaped kite.
12. **e** Each picture contains dotted lines.

- ## Section 3 Test 4 (pages 34–35)

1. **b** The shapes get **lighter**.
2. **e** teddy bear, doll, teddy bear, doll, **teddy bear**
3. **a** scissors, crayons, scissors, crayons, **scissors**
4. **c** large upright parallelogram, small parallelogram, large upright parallelogram, small parallelogram, **large upright parallelogram**
5. **a** The elephants get **bigger** and all face left.
6. **d** white upright heart, black upright heart, white upright heart, black upright heart, **white upright heart**
7. **b**

8. **a**

9. **e**

10. **a**

11. **d**

12. **b**

Section 3 Test 5 (pages 36–37)

1. d

2. e

3. b

4. e

5. c

6. b

7. c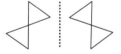

8. a

9. d

10. d

11. a

12. b

Section 3 Test 6 (pages 38–39)

1. c

2. c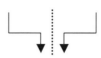

3. a

4. d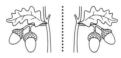

5. d

6. c

7. b The fish get **smaller** and face left.

8. b trunk left, trunk up, trunk left, trunk up, **trunk left**

9. e two small crosses with left higher, one large cross, two small crosses with left higher, one large cross, **two small crosses with left higher**

10. b tail up, tail down, tail up, tail down, **tail up** (and facing left)

11. a black arrow right, white arrow down, black arrow right, white arrow down, **black arrow right**

12. b single point up, single point down, single point up, single point down, **single point up** (white star)

This book of answers is a pull-out section from
Rapid Reasoning Tests: Non-verbal Reasoning 1

Published by Schofield & Sims Ltd,
Dogley Mill, Fenay Bridge, Huddersfield HD8 0NQ, UK
Telephone 01484 607080

www.schofieldandsims.co.uk

Second impression 2014
Copyright © Schofield & Sims Ltd, 2014

Author: **Rebecca Brant**
Rebecca Brant has asserted her moral right under the Copyright, Designs and Patents Act, 1988, to be identified as the author of this work.

British Library Cataloguing in Publication Data
A catalogue record for this book is available from the British Library.

Commissioned by **Carolyn Richardson Publishing Services** *(www.publiserve.co.uk)*

Design by **Oxford Designers & Illustrators**
Printed in the UK by **The Lavenham Press Ltd**, *Suffolk*

ISBN 978 07217 1226 0

■ Which picture on the right belongs to the group on the left? Circle the letter.

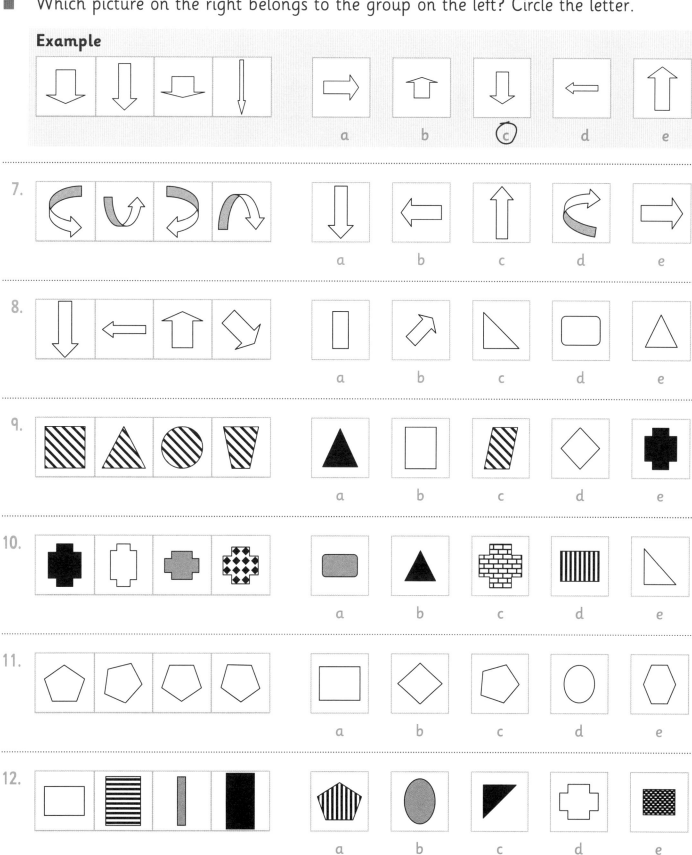

End of test.

Score:	Time taken:	Target met?

Target time: **5 minutes**

Which picture on the right goes in the empty space? Circle the letter.

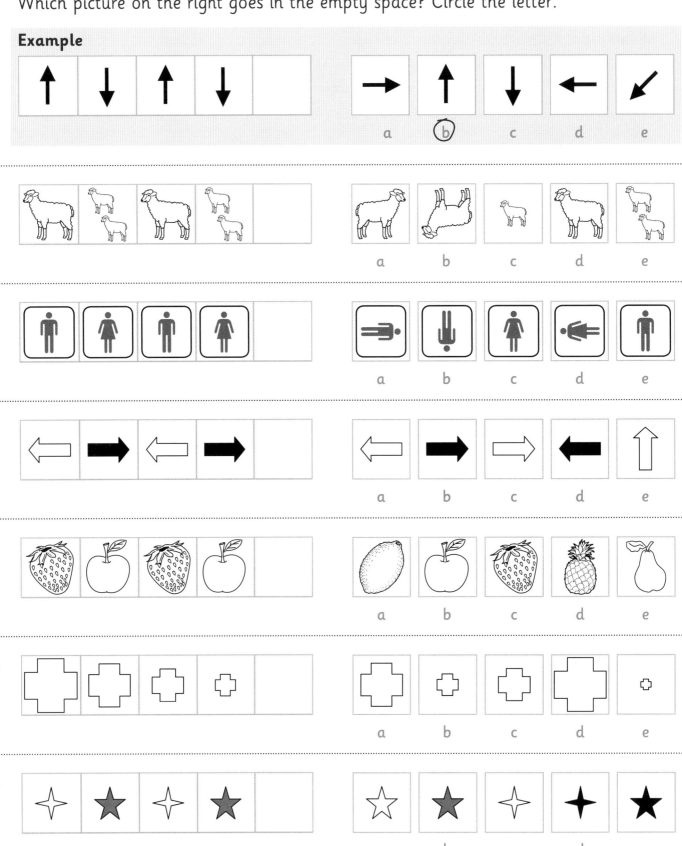

■ In which picture on the right is the picture on the left hidden? Circle the letter.

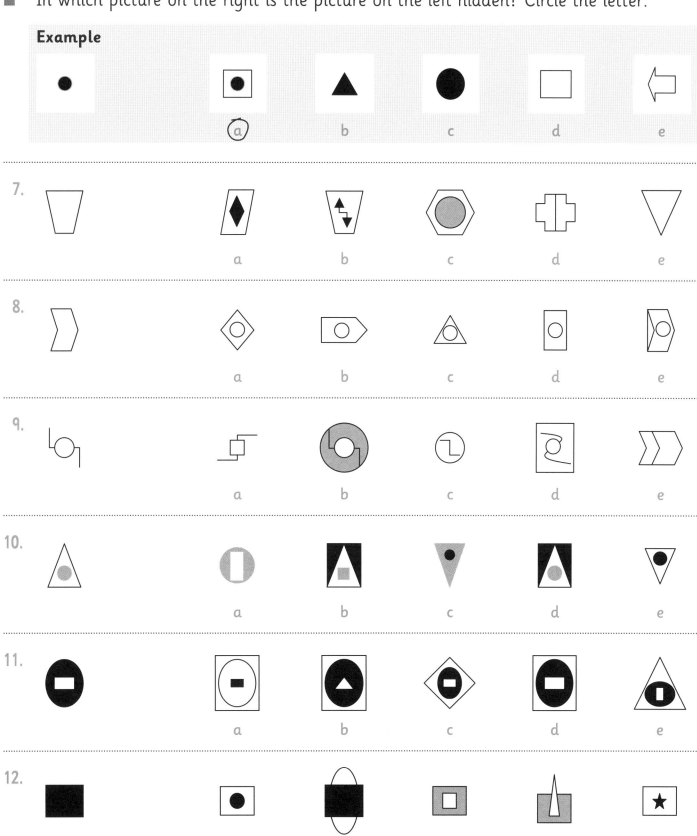

Example

7.

8.

9.

10.

11.

12.

End of test.

Score:	Time taken:	Target met?

In which picture on the right is the picture on the left hidden? Circle the letter.

Example

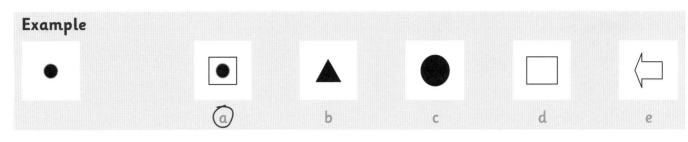

ⓐ	b	c	d	e

1.

a   b   c   d   e

2.

a   b   c   d   e

3.

a   b   c   d   e

4.

a   b   c   d   e

5.

a   b   c   d   e

6.

a   b   c   d   e

Now go on to the next page. ➡

■ Pretend the dotted line is a mirror. Which picture on the right is a reflection of the picture on the left? Circle the letter.

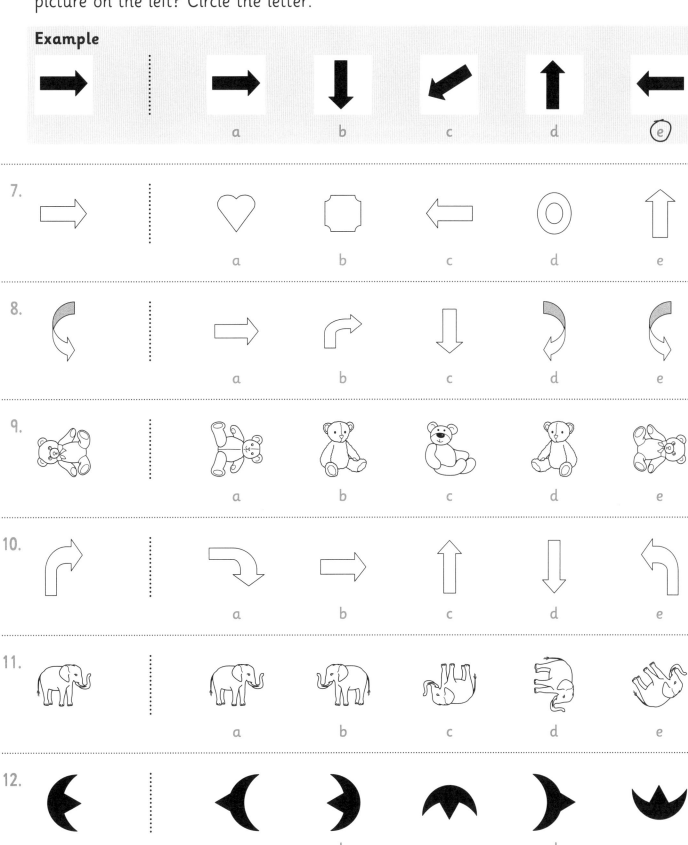

Example

| | a | b | c | d | e |

7.

8.

9.

10.

11.

12.

End of test.

| Score: | | Time taken: | | Target met? | |

Pretend the dotted line is a mirror. Which picture on the right is a reflection of the picture on the left? Circle the letter.

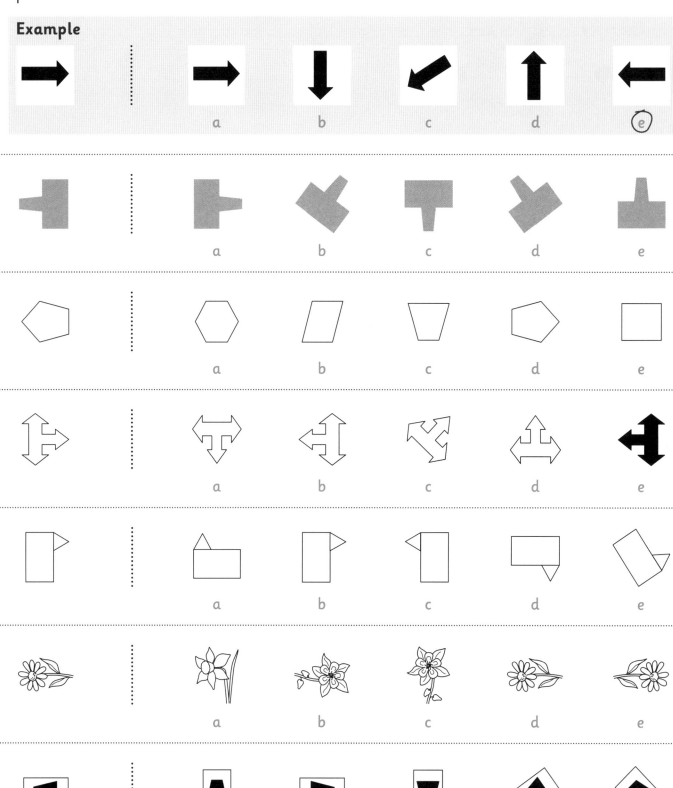

Example

a   b   c   d   (e)

1.   a   b   c   d   e

2.   a   b   c   d   e

3.   a   b   c   d   e

4.   a   b   c   d   e

5.   a   b   c   d   e

6.   a   b   c   d   e

Now go on to the next page. ➡

■ Which of the pictures on the right goes in the empty space? Circle the letter.

Example

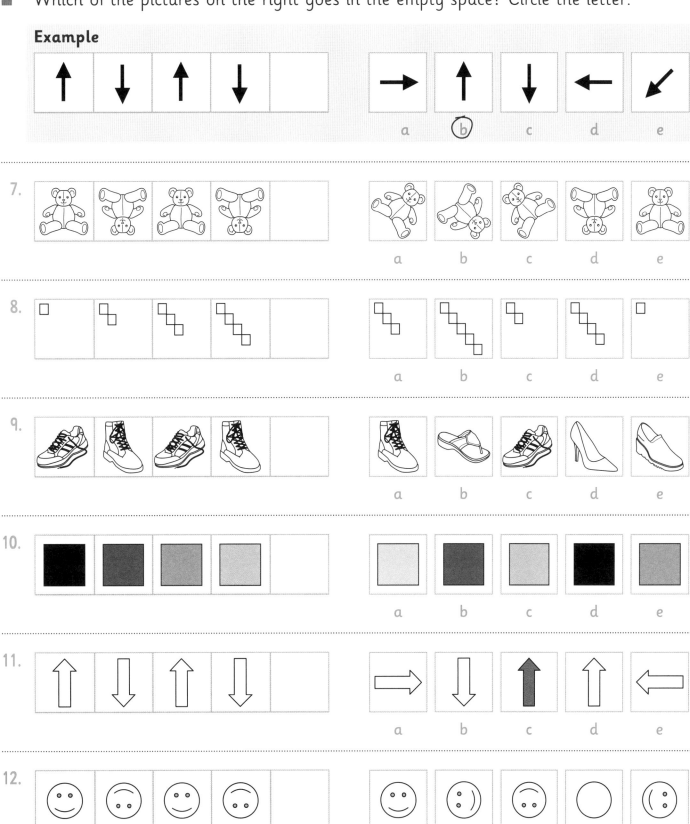

End of test.

Score:		Time taken:		Target met?	

Target time: **5 minutes**

Which picture on the right belongs to the group on the left? Circle the letter.

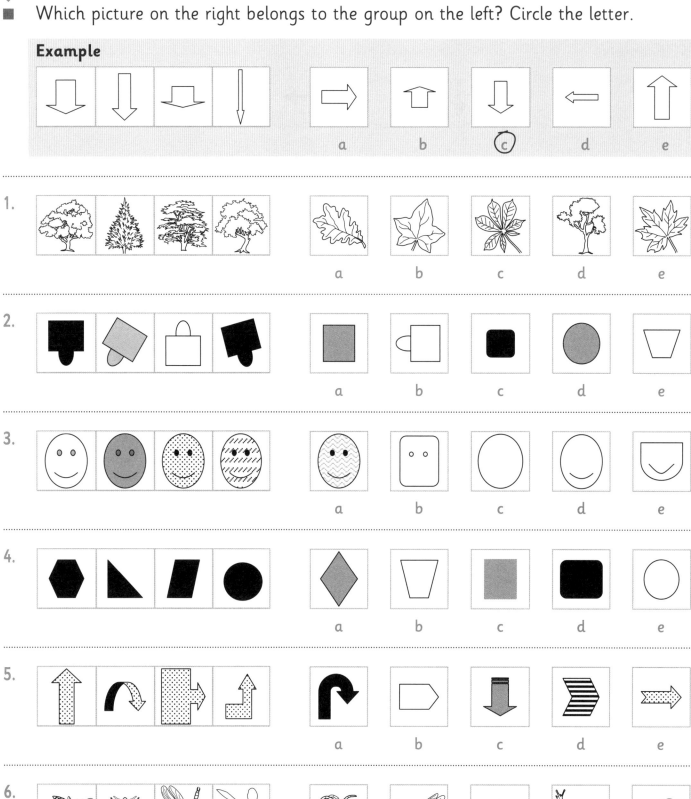

Example

1.

2.

3.

4.

5.

6.

Now go on to the next page. ➡

■ Which picture is the odd one out? Circle the letter.

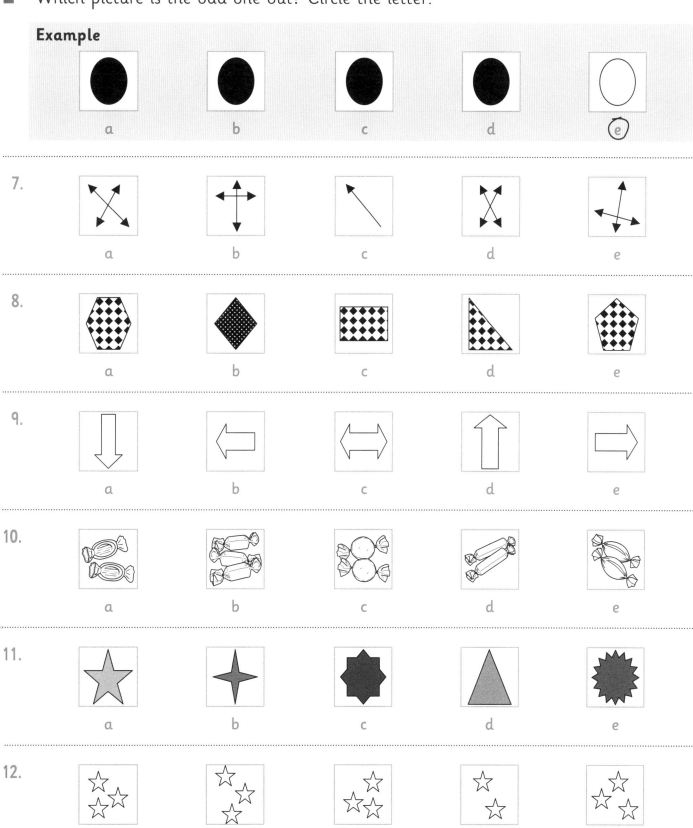

Example

| a | b | c | d | e |

7. a b c d e

8. a b c d e

9. a b c d e

10. a b c d e

11. a b c d e

12. a b c d e

End of test.

| Score: | Time taken: | Target met? |

Which picture is the odd one out? Circle the letter.

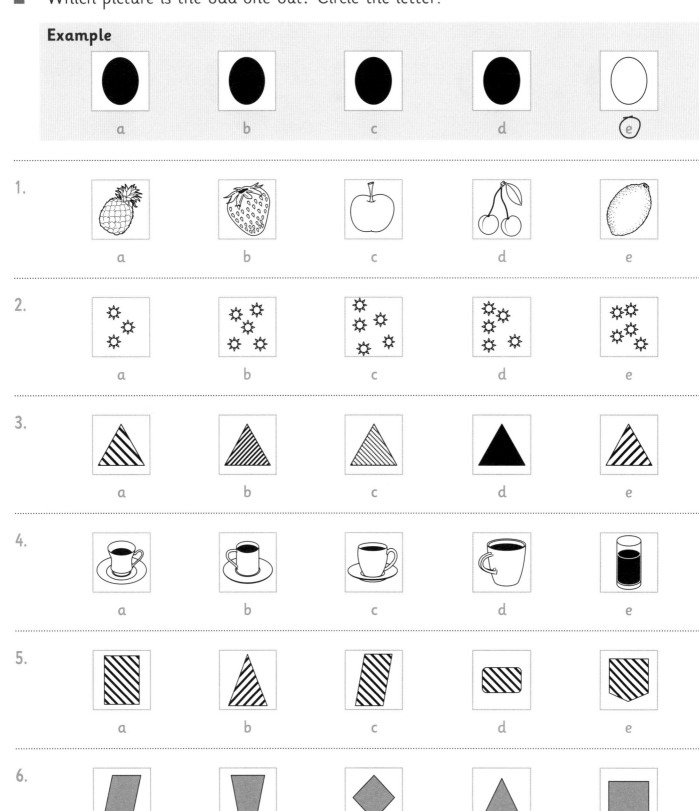

Example

a   b   c   d   (e)

1. a   b   c   d   e

2. a   b   c   d   e

3. a   b   c   d   e

4. a   b   c   d   e

5. a   b   c   d   e

6. a   b   c   d   e

Now go on to the next page. ➡

The first two pictures go together. Which of the five pictures on the right goes with the third picture in the same way? Circle the letter.

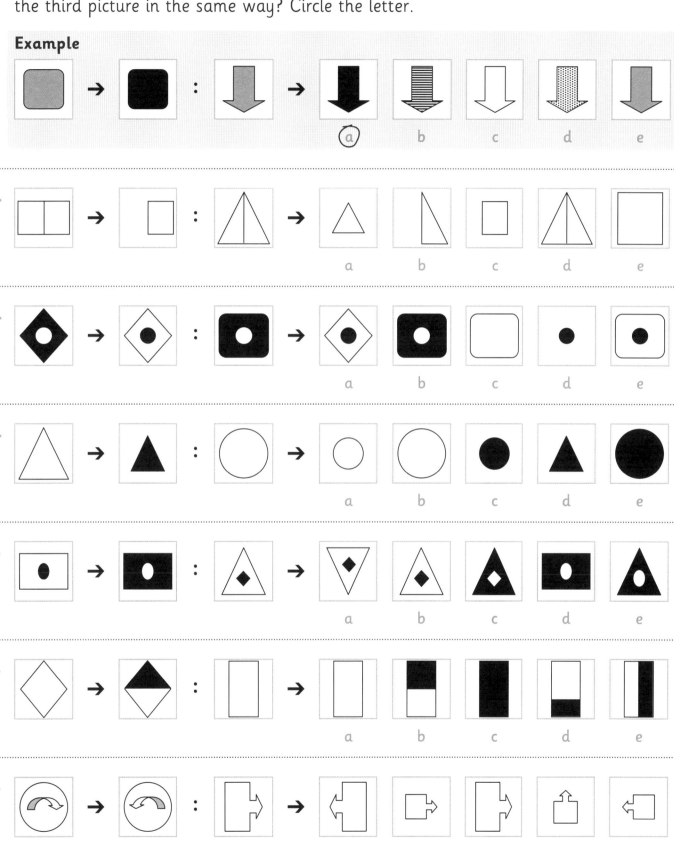

End of test.

| Score: | | Time taken: | | Target met? | |

The first two pictures go together. Which of the five pictures on the right goes with the third picture in the same way? Circle the letter.

Example

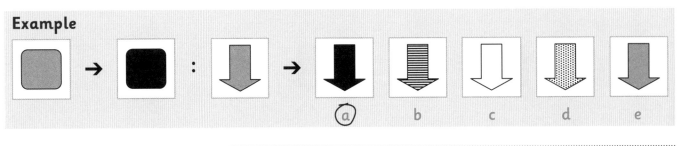

1.

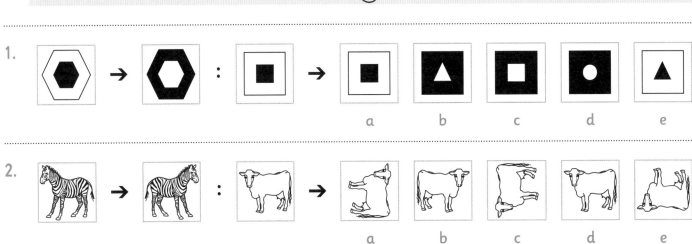

2.

3.

4.

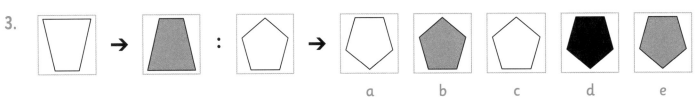

5.

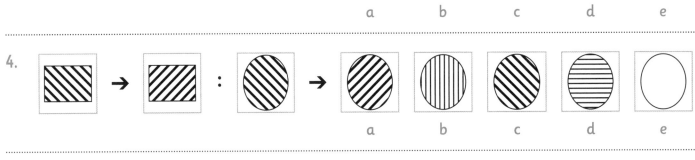

6.

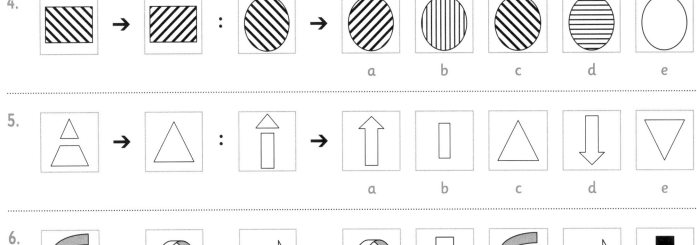

Now go on to the next page.

■ Which picture on the right belongs to the group on the left? Circle the letter.

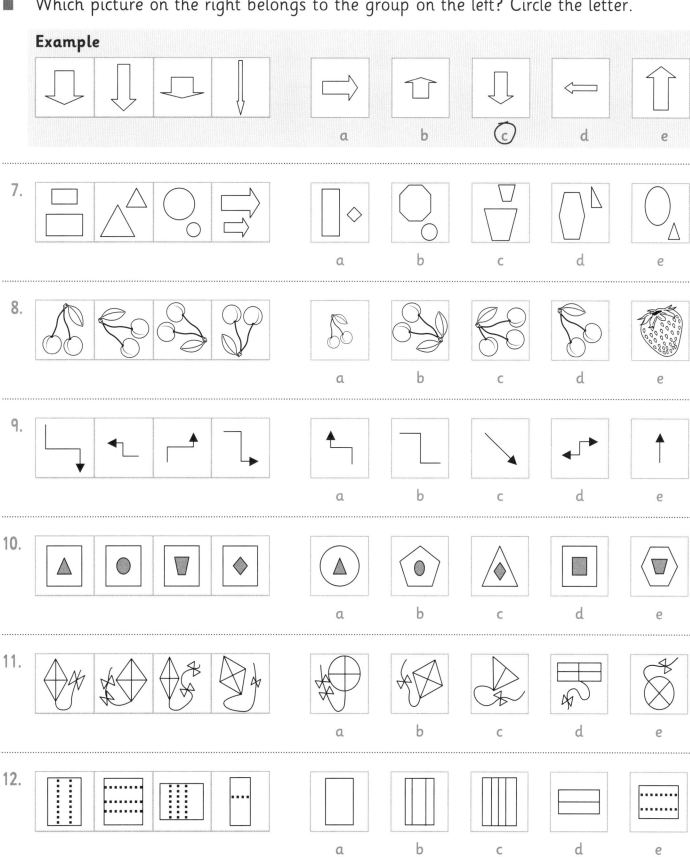

Example

a   b   c   d   e

7.

a   b   c   d   e

8.

a   b   c   d   e

9.

a   b   c   d   e

10.

a   b   c   d   e

11.

a   b   c   d   e

12.

a   b   c   d   e

End of test.

Score:	Time taken:	Target met?

Target time: **5 minutes**

Which of the pictures on the right goes in the empty space? Circle the letter.

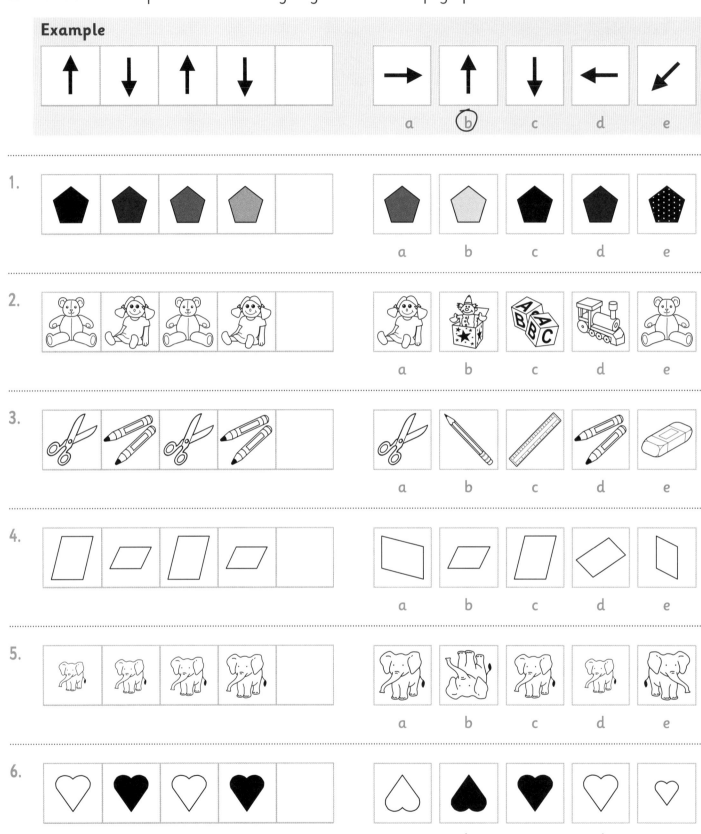

Example

a   b   c   d   e

1.

a   b   c   d   e

2.

a   b   c   d   e

3.

a   b   c   d   e

4.

a   b   c   d   e

5.

a   b   c   d   e

6.

a   b   c   d   e

Now go on to the next page.

■ In which picture on the right is the picture on the left hidden? Circle the letter.

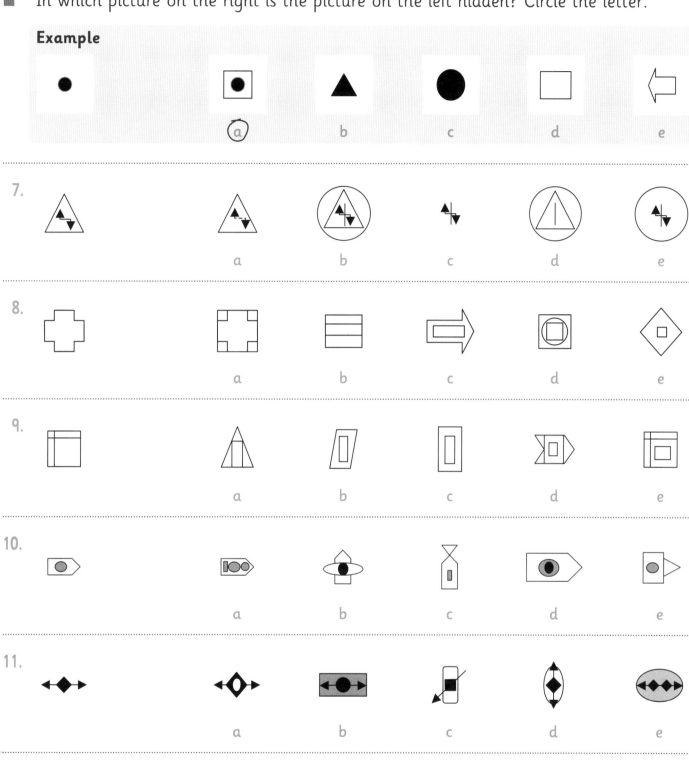

Example

a   b   c   d   e

7.

a   b   c   d   e

8.

a   b   c   d   e

9.

a   b   c   d   e

10.

a   b   c   d   e

11.

a   b   c   d   e

12.

a   b   c   d   e

End of test.

Score:		Time taken:		Target met?	

In which picture on the right is the picture on the left hidden? Circle the letter.

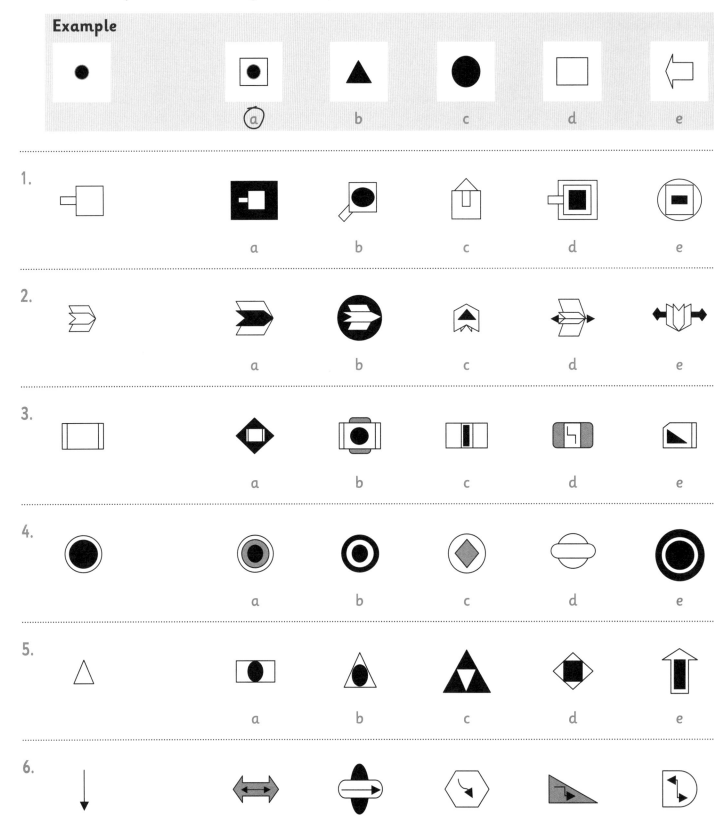

Example

a b c d e

1.

a b c d e

2.

a b c d e

3.

a b c d e

4.

a b c d e

5.

a b c d e

6.

a b c d e

Now go on to the next page. ➡

Pretend the dotted line is a mirror. Which picture on the right is a reflection of the picture on the left? Circle the letter.

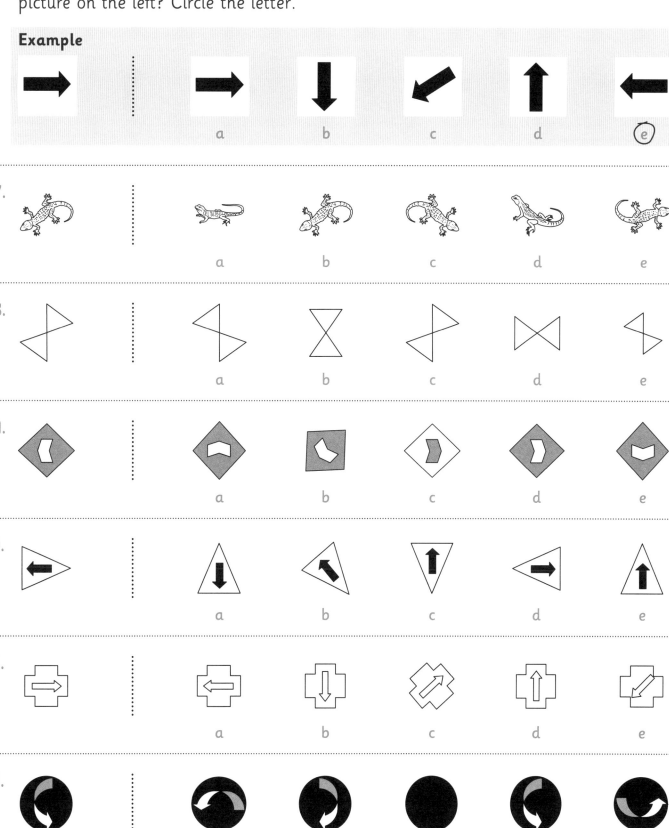

Example

a   b   c   d   e

7.   a   b   c   d   e

8.   a   b   c   d   e

9.   a   b   c   d   e

10.   a   b   c   d   e

11.   a   b   c   d   e

12.   a   b   c   d   e

End of test.

Score:	Time taken:	Target met?

Pretend the dotted line is a mirror. Which picture on the right is a reflection of the picture on the left? Circle the letter.

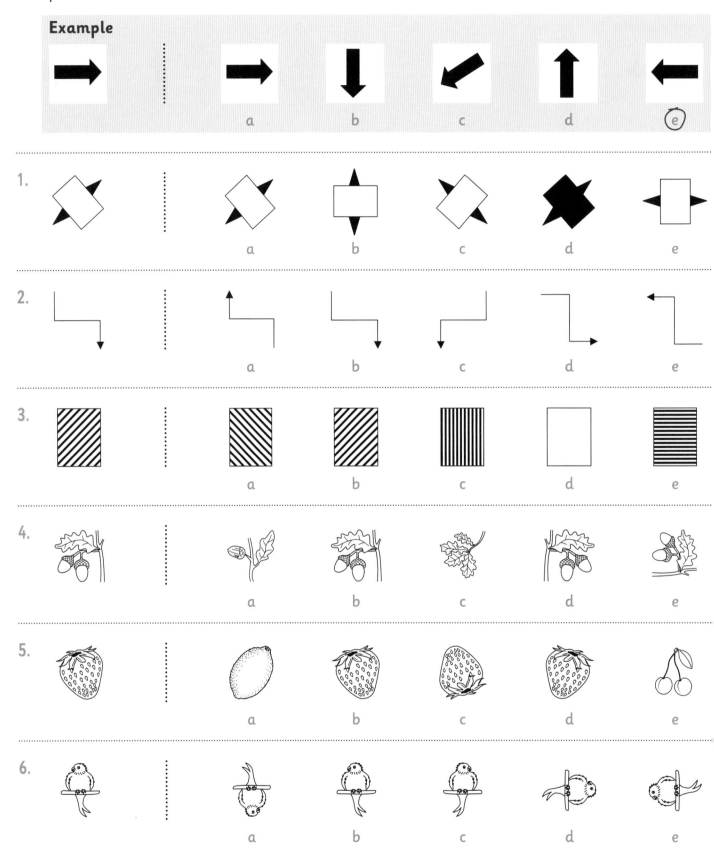

Example

Now go on to the next page. ➡

■ Which picture on the right goes in the empty space? Circle the letter.

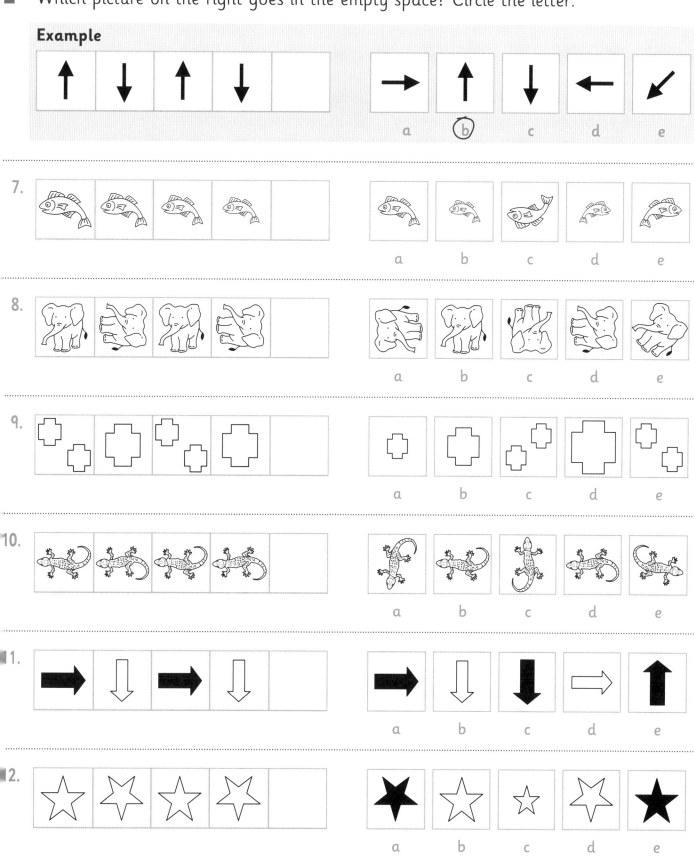

End of test.

| Score: | | Time taken: | | Target met? | |

Schofield&Sims

the long-established educational publisher specialising in maths, English and science

Non-verbal Reasoning 1 is a collection of short, problem-solving tests based on pictures and patterns. Each timed test includes age-appropriate questions, providing opportunities for children to practise and master non-verbal reasoning skills in preparation for the 11+ and other school selection tests. The first of six non-verbal reasoning books in the **Rapid Reasoning Tests** series, this book covers the following question types: similarities and differences; missing and hidden shapes; cubes, codes and combinations.

Rapid Reasoning Tests provides short, effective, timed tests in reasoning. The series comprises six books of verbal reasoning tests and six books of non-verbal reasoning tests.

Written by experienced teachers and designed for independent use, **Rapid Reasoning Tests** has been carefully structured to provide practice of key, standard format question types. Each collection of tests has been designed for use over one year and provides one section per term in order to support regular practice.

Key features

- **Short tests** requiring few resources that are easy to fit into a busy timetable.
- A **target time** for each test encourages children to work quickly and develop the necessary exam skills for success in the 11+ and other tests.
- **Pull-out answers** in the centre of each book can be easily removed.
- **Free downloads** to support the series are available from the Schofield & Sims website.

The full series includes the following books:

Verbal Reasoning 1 978 07217 1238 3	**Non-verbal Reasoning 1** 978 07217 1226 0 **(Ages 6–7)**
Verbal Reasoning 2 978 07217 1239 0	**Non-verbal Reasoning 2** 978 07217 1227 7 **(Ages 7–8)**
Verbal Reasoning 3 978 07217 1313 7	**Non-verbal Reasoning 3** 978 07217 1228 4 **(Ages 8–9)**
Verbal Reasoning 4 978 07217 1241 3	**Non-verbal Reasoning 4** 978 07217 1229 1 **(Ages 9–10)**
Verbal Reasoning 5 978 07217 1242 0	**Non-verbal Reasoning 5** 978 07217 1230 7 **(Ages 10–11)**
Verbal Reasoning 6 978 07217 1243 7	**Non-verbal Reasoning 6** 978 07217 1231 4 **(Ages 11–12)**

MIX
Paper from responsible sources
FSC® C010693
www.fsc.org

ISBN 978-07217-1226-0

9 780721 712260 >

ISBN 978 07217 1226 0
Key Stage 1
Age range 6–7
£3.95
(Retail price)

For further information and to place an order visit
www.schofieldandsims.co.uk or telephone 01484 607080